To my darling Mark,
happy reading!

Cruia Stan

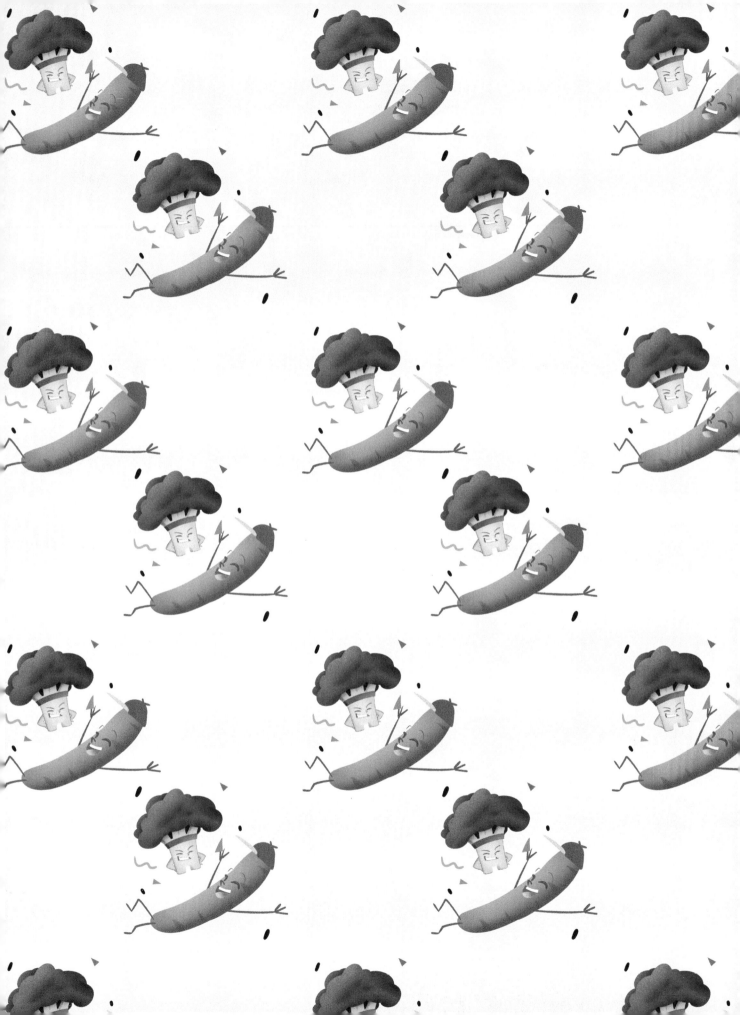

THIS MISCHIEVOUS STORY BOOK BELONGS TO:

_____

Reading with your child
Tips for sharing this book

Look at the cover. What do your little listeners think actually happens in the story? Talk about what could possibly go wrong if the veggies have a fight inside the fridge.

Ask them about food preferences: do they like broccoli, beans, and sausages? What is their favourite food and would it go well with broccoli on top? (especially if they answer ICE CREAM!)

Throughout the story, encourage them to guess what happens next and describe what they see in the pictures.

At the end, talk to them about the meaning of the story, discuss the beauty of friendship, believing in your friends and working together, but also the importance of eating healthy foods and vegetables.

After reading the story, don't forget to check out the Fun Facts section for some cool veggie knowledge, and Mama's healthy, hearty dinner recipes at the back of this book for your very own cook at home adventure with the kids!

Look at me!
I'm so cute!

The Veggie Mischief

Corina Stanescu
Illustrated by Bianca Silva

For Mircea,
Thank you for always believing in me.

First published by Teeny Books in Great Britain, 2023.
www.teenybooks.com

Written by Corina Stanescu
Illustrated by Bianca Silva

ISBN: 9781399961882

ISBN 978-1-3999-6188-2

9 781399 961882

Who is in this story?

Brocco
A cheeky vegetable with big plans to take over the dinner table

Ben The Beans Price
The best friend any vegetable would love to have

Mannie
The handsome sausage who gets all the love

Ricelina the Rice Queen
The magic fairy who fixes all their problems

Chad
The dude who's there just for the show. So cheesy!

Now let's meet the
Mischievous Friends!

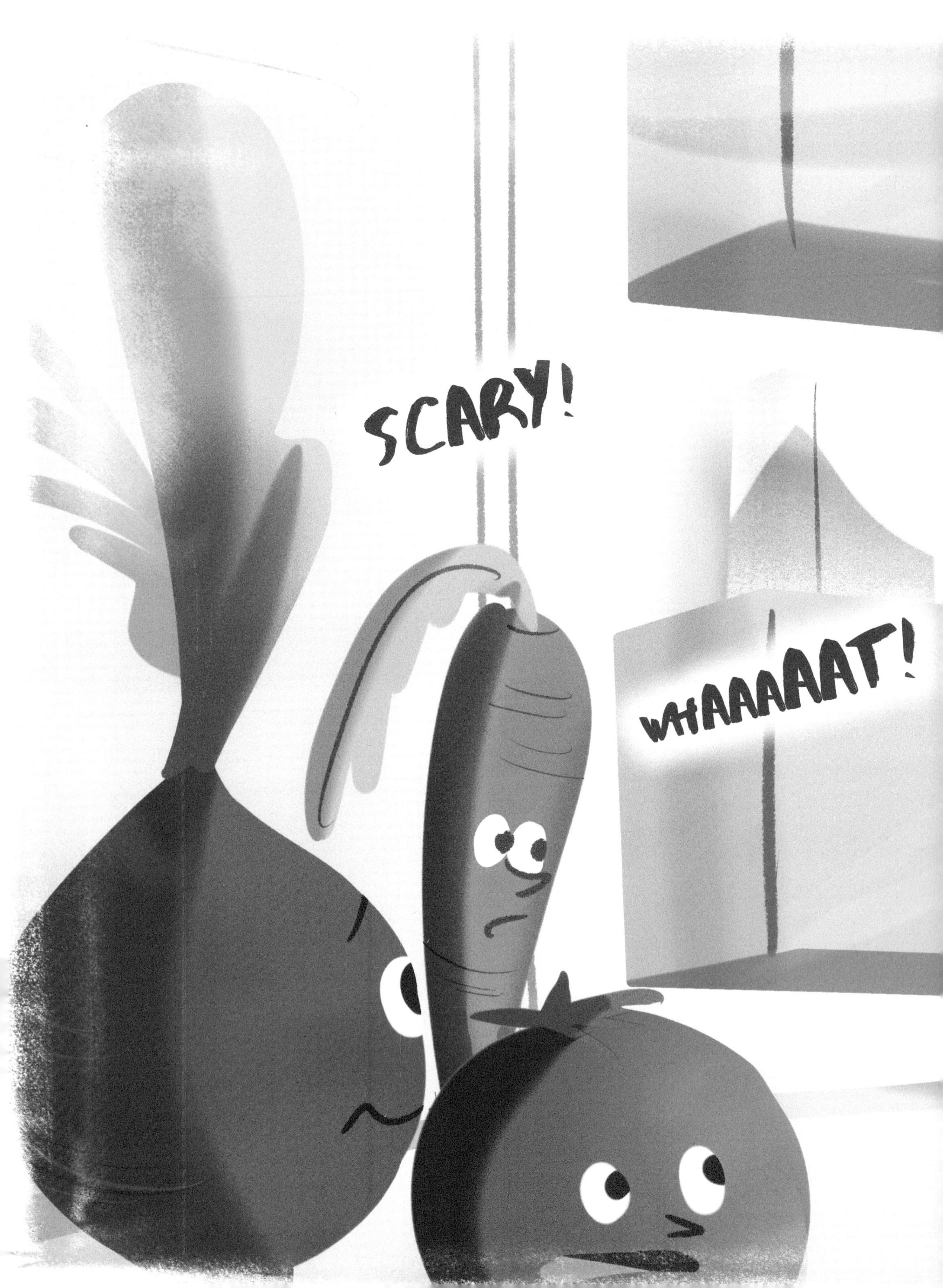
SCARY!
WHAAAAAT!

Brocco is a **GONE BAD** vegetable, the kind that stares at you from the back of the fridge with a mean grin, threatening to spread evil all around the other veggies.

He is a massive broccoli head famous for his loud, farty sounds, and his nasty smells. And today, he's about to get **EXTRA MISCHIEVOUS**.

Ben the Beans Prince is tiny and brown, and rather cute. He lives in a saucy tin, in the fridge.

Ben is Brocco's best friend, and he doesn't actually believe Brocco is bad. He knows Brocco is feeling a bit lonely, and misses being picked for dinner.

Mannie is the handsome sausage who always gets chosen for dinner. But Brocco is determined to change this today and he came up with a mischievous plan to make sure **HE** will be the one picked for dinner instead.

All Brocco needs to do now is convince Ben to join him in bombarding Mannie ...**WITH LOUD, SMELLY FARTS.**

Meanwhile, Mannie is very excited as he overheard Susie, the little girl who opens their fridge everyday, say something about "sausages are my favourite" and "I don't like the green stuff".

So Mannie is sure he'll get picked again for dinner today. Little does he know that Brocco has **OTHER PLANS...**

But Brocco also heard Susie and with Ben's help, he is planning to fill Mannie's fridge drawer with rotten broccoli and bean smells, leaving him **SMELLY AND UNFIT** for dinner.

"Come on, Ben! Let's do this!
It serves him and his spicy attitude just right", said Brocco
encouraging Ben to join in.

Ben wasn't really sure this was the best way to fix
Brocco's problem, but it sounded kind of fun, so he went
along with it.

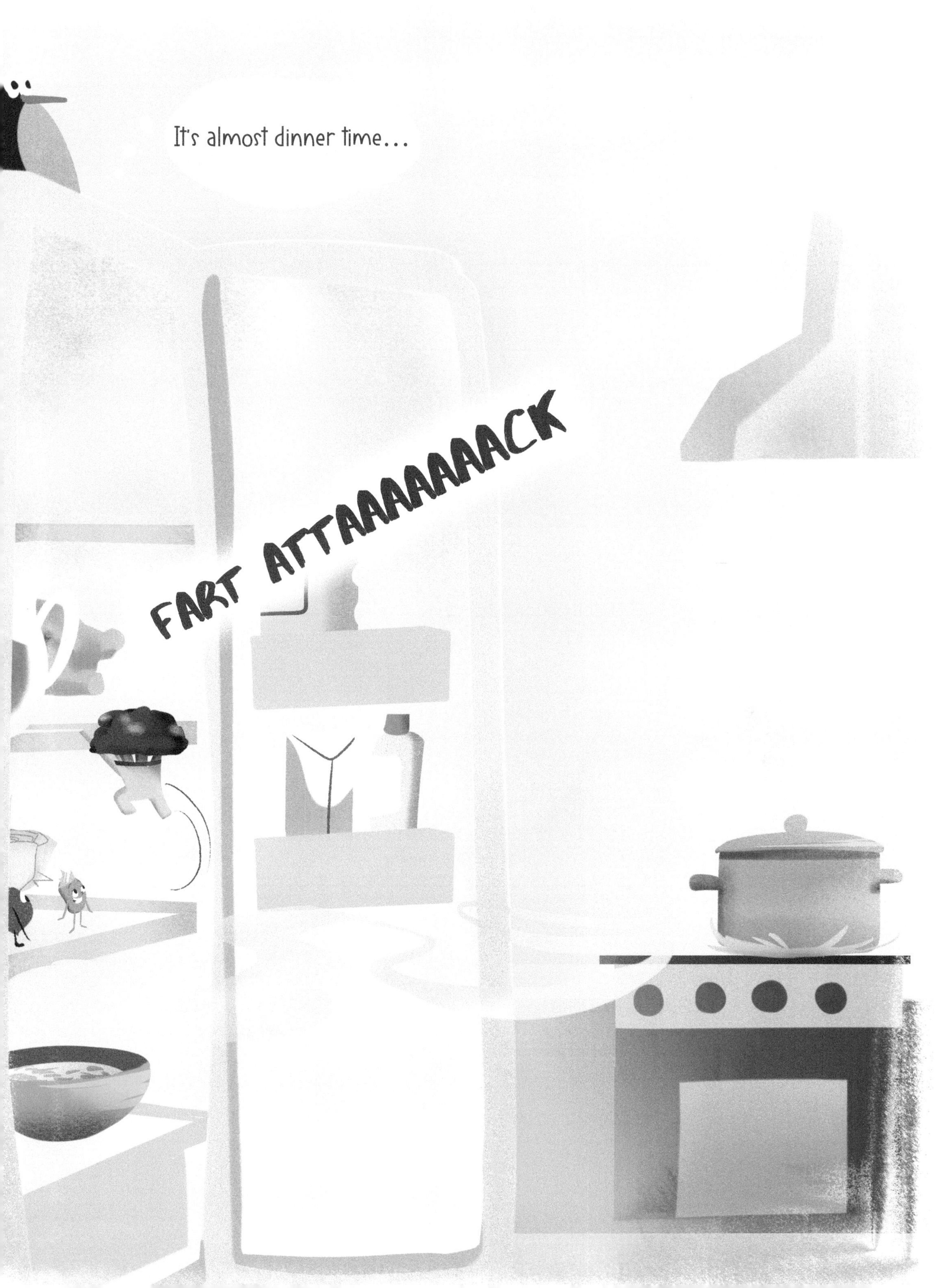
It's almost dinner time…
FART ATTAAAAAAACK

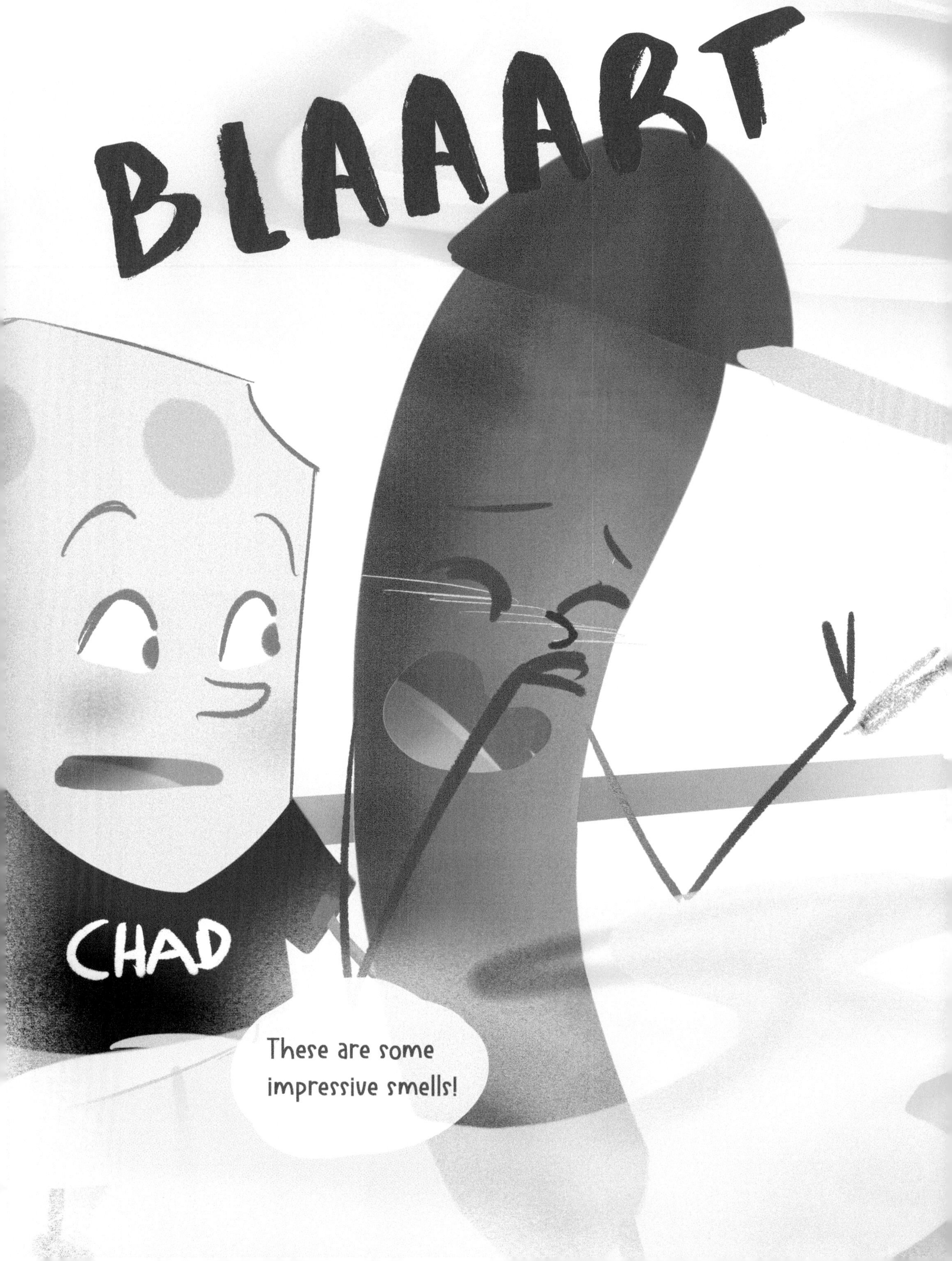
BLAAART
CHAD
These are some impressive smells!

One thousand or maybe two thousand stinky smells and fart noises later, the gang concluded it was a terrible success and that the entire fridge now smells **HORRIBLY**.

Even Chad the Cheese was impressed and said he might join in next time, just for the fun of it.

BLAAART

Shortly after, Susie opened the fridge and exclaimed:
"Oh, what a smell! Mama, I think the sausage has gone bad...

REALLY, REALLY BAD!"

Mama took Mannie out and gave him a sniff. She noticed he was fine outside of the fridge. She then sniffed the drawer, and checked the vegetables too.

"Darling, I think I found the culprits here: **THE VEGGIES!** I'd better put these in the bin," said Mama.

Oh no, this is not going as planned...

Ben knew that deep down Brocco was a very good veggie, so he called for his friend, Ricelina the Rice Queen's help immediately.

From her cupboard up high, Ricelina responded happily,
"It's about time Susie sees Brocco for the good veggie that he
is! Better get ready, dinner friends...

.... IT'S MAGIC TIME!"

BBiSH

Ricelina then waved her wand and a
magic cloud appeared in Mama's kitchen.

With a little bit of magic from Ricelina, Mama had a brilliant idea and said:

"Instead of putting this broccoli in the bin, how about I clean this bad boy up by removing all his bad bits? I'll make him good to cook with some rice in no time!"

"Then we can add the sausage in a pan with some beans and some tomato sauce...

... and **TA-DA!**
A healthy, hearty, full of vegetable dinner is ready!"

Susie laughed and said:

"And next time we can do that before all the
veggies go bad and start a fart attack in the
fridge!"

HA HA HA

SALT

Susie finished all her dinner that evening, and went to bed with a happy tummy.

Brocco felt **GOOD** for the first time in a long time. He was now a happy vegetable, and understood that dinner time is more fun when they all work together as friends and everyone gets a spot on the table.

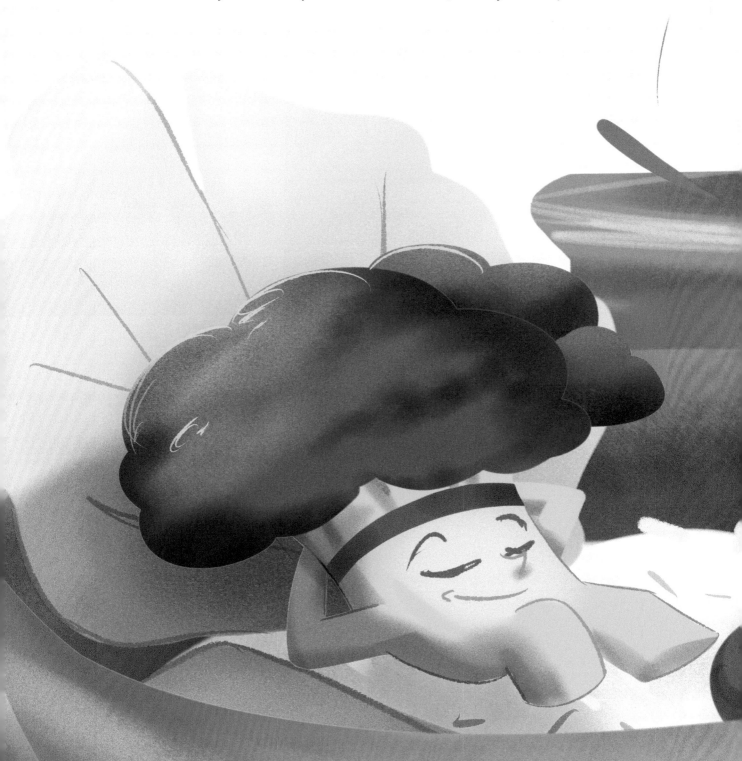

Ben and Mannie happily swam together in a casserole, having loads of fun and Ricelina was very pleased her magic made Brocco feel like a good vegetable again.

The bad veggie days were gone **FOREVER!**

THE END

Fun Facts
About Our Dinner Friends

BROCCOLI is one of the healthiest vegetables to help your body and your bones grow big and strong! And not only that, it also works to protect you from nasty viruses and germs. Have some with your dinner tomorrow and see how much stronger you feel after!

BEANS are the royalty of legumes, easy to find everywhere and delicious. Did you know that ancient warriors ate a lot of beans to make them super strong? Beans also give you lots of energy to be super fast on the playground!

Woow, we're super healthy, Ben!

SAUSAGES are a tasty way to add more muscle power to your dinners, and they go really well with your warrior food, the beans. Did you know that you can make sausages at home, using all plants or meat ingredients too?

I'm so tasty I could bite myself!

RICE is super healthy and probably the most common food around the world, feeding more than half of people EVERYWHERE! It originally came from Asia, and now everyone loves it because it's delicious, easy to cook, goes well with any veggie and keeps you full of energy to run around with your friends!

HOW ABOUT COOKING Mama's super healthy dishes for dinner? Check out the easy beansy recipes on the next pages!

Mannie and Ben Dinner Casserole

INGREDIENTS:

1 tablespoon oil
8 Mannies aka sausages (meat, veggie or vegan)
1 onion, diced
2 garlic cloves, crushed
2 medium carrots, chopped
400g tinned chopped tomatoes
1 tablespoon tomato paste
200ml stock or just water
½ teaspoon paprika
½ teaspoon dried mixed herbs
400g tinned Bens, oh I mean beans

HA HA HA

What is red and goes up
and down?
A tomato in an elevator.

HOW TO MAKE IT

Heat the oil in a large saucepan. Add the Mannies and fry for 5-6 minutes until they start to brown. Remove them from the pan and set aside.

Chopped whaaat?!

In the same pan, add the onions and fry for 2-3 minutes until they soften. Then add the garlic and chooped carrots and cook for another 2 minutes.

Dreamy!

Add the tinned tomatoes, tomato paste, stock, paprika and mixed herbs. Stir well before adding the Mannies back in. Cook on a low-medium heat for 15 minutes.
Add the Bens, erm.. beans and cook for a further 5 minutes until they have warmed through.

Serve immediately with crusty bread or Ricelinas. I mean rice.

Brocco and Ricelina Dinner Dish

INGREDIENTS:

2 cups of rice, also known as Ricelinas
3 cups water or stock
1 mighty Brocco, chopped
1/2 white onion, chopped
2 tablespoons of butter or olive oil
1 garlic clove crushed, or 1/4 teaspoon of garlic powder
1/2 teaspoon salt

Optional: 1/4 cup of grated Chad

HA HA HA

What do you call
an onion that likes karate?
A chopped onion!

That joke stinks!

HOW TO MAKE IT

Place the Ricelinas in a large pot and add 3 cups of water or stock. Place a lid on the pot and bring it up to a boil over high heat.

Once it reaches a boil, turn the heat down to low, and let it simmer for 15 minutes. After that, turn the heat off and let the rice rest without removing the lid for another 5 minutes.

While the Ricelinas are cooking, put the oil or butter into a frying pan, add in the onions and chopped Brocco and fry for 2-3 mins.

Once the rice has cooked, fluff it gently with a fork. Add the onions, Brocco, salt and garlic powder.

If you like your rice a little cheesy, add your grated Chad now.

Serve immediately to hungry tummies.

Hope you had a blast reading this
mischievous veggie story and enjoyed the fun facts
about our dinner friends.

Now it's time for **YOU** to start your own veggie adventure
and pack in those healthy dinners to fuel you up
for extra fun on the playground!

Oh, and if you're a dino fan who loves a good
giggle, you might want to check out
Rawry's Missing Tooth from the same author